Practise Reading

Colour each picture as you finish each page.

Written by Jillian Harker and Geraldine Taylor
Illustrated by Colin Robinson

Ladybird

The farm

Can you read this?
Ask a grown-up to help you.

Welcome to Uphill Farm.
The Carter family lives here. You will meet
them and many of their animals in this book.
Uphill Farm is on top of a hill near a very large wood
called Puzzle Wood. Lots of children come to visit the farm.

Have you ever visited a farm?
Do you know what farmers do?

Follow the alphabet through Puzzle Wood
to find your way to Uphill Farm.

Meet Mr Carter

Mr Carter takes care of the animals at Uphill Farm. He has to get up early in the morning because he has so much to do.

He has to look after all these animals at Uphill Farm – cows, pigs, sheep, hens, geese, ducks, goats and horses.

What time did you get up this morning? Do you have a pet to look after?

Mr Carter wants some signs to help the children
who visit the farm. Can you write these for him?

Meet Mrs Carter

Mrs Carter is in the dairy. She churns milk to make butter.
Then she presses the cheese in the cheese press.
Children like to watch her work and chat to her.
Mrs Carter cuts them a chunk of cheese with a sharp knife.

Do you like the taste of cheese?

Write either **ch** or **sh** in front of these letters and
read the words. Can you find the things in the picture?

ch

_ _ air

_ _ icken

_ _ unk

_ _ ick

_ _ ildren

_ _ eese

sh

_ _ eep

_ _ elf

_ _ ip

_ _ irt

_ _ oes

> Did you find the chick?

Meet Katy Carter

Katy Carter is working in the garden to help her
mother and father. She is weeding the rows and digging
a new patch of earth. She is planting some seeds
and watering them. Now she is picking the beans.
Last of all she is pulling up some carrots.

Have you ever planted seeds?

Can you remember what Katy is doing?
Write the missing words.

Katy is _____

in the garden.

Katy is _____ and

_____ the seeds.

Katy is _____

the rows.

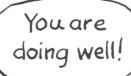

Katy is _____

the beans.

Katy is _____

up the carrots.

You are doing well!

Meet George Carter

George Carter is Katy's brother. He is getting ready
to go to the market with his sister. He is writing a list of
all the things from the farm that he wants to sell.
He will pack them in boxes and load them into the van.
His grandmother will drive them all to market.

Is there a market near you?

This is George's list.

Tick what you would like to buy.

Write your name and your own shopping list here.

bread ☐
eggs ☐
lettuce ☐
cheese ☐
apples ☐
carrots ☐
plums ☐
fruit pies ☐
butter ☐

_____'s list

Plums are my favourite.

Meet Grandmother Carter

Grandmother Carter sets up the farm stall
at the market. Katy and George help their
grandmother to unpack the boxes and to sell
the goods. They like it best when lots of people
come to buy. Some people come each week
to buy their favourite Uphill Farm fruit pies and bread.

What is your favourite food?

Can you find the Carters' stall?
Read these clues to help you.

The stall is blue.
The stall is not in the middle row.
The stall is not near the supermarket.
The stall is not next to the seats.
The stall is near one tree.
The stall is in a corner.

Did you find our stall?

Circle the Carters' stall
when you find it.

Meet Grandfather Carter

Grandfather Carter is not at the market today.
He is going to drive his tractor to the fields to harvest
the crops. He looks at the blue sky and hopes it will
not rain. Grandfather Carter must work hard to
bring in the harvest while the weather is fine.

He has a special harvest song which he likes
to sing on his tractor.

Which songs do you like to sing?

Can you read and remember
Grandfather Carter's special
harvest song?

Rain, rain go away
It's Uphill Farm's harvest day

Up and down the fields I go
Bringing crops in row by row

The sky is blue, the sun is warm
No black clouds to start a storm

Up and down the fields I go
Bringing crops in row by row

What a good
memory you have.

Meet Tiptoes the farm cat

Tiptoes is a friendly black cat with white fur on her feet.
She looks as though she is wearing socks.
Visitors can usually find her near the farmhouse
or around the barn. She chases the mice
and plays with the children, but most of all
she likes to lie in the sun and sleep.

Where have you seen a cat sleeping?

Where do you think Tiptoes would like to sleep?
Tick the boxes.

Inside the kitchen ☐

On a sunny window sill ☐

In a cool corner ☐

In a hot spot in the yard ☐

In a warm place on the lawn ☐

In the shade of a tree ☐

Purr-fect!

Meet Tricks the sheepdog

Tricks the sheepdog helps Mr Carter look after the sheep at Uphill Farm. He makes sure that the sheep go where Mr Carter wants them to go. He has been working with Mr Carter for a very long time.

Have you ever seen a sheepdog at work?

Sheepdog facts

1 Sheepdogs are usually collies.

2 You must begin to train a sheepdog when it is a puppy.

3 Sheepdogs sleep in a kennel.

4 Sheepdogs are used to guard and herd sheep.

5 The farmer uses special whistles to talk to his dogs and tell them what to do.

Can you find the words coloured blue in a dictionary? Ask a grown-up to help you.

Circle the picture that answers each question.

1 Where do sheepdogs sleep?

 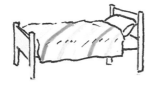

2 How do farmers talk to sheepdogs?

3 When do you start to train a sheepdog?

4 What do sheepdogs do?

Meet the visitors

These children go to school in a large town. Today they have come by coach to visit Uphill Farm with their teacher. The Carter family is taking it in turns to show them round the farm.

Mr Carter shows some of the children his sheep and cows, and Mrs Carter makes cheese with another group.

Katy takes some children to collect eggs with her, and George takes two children to see a new-born gosling. There are lots of baby animals on the farm.

Have you ever been on a school trip?

The teacher has asked the children to fill in this worksheet. Can you do it too?

goats

sheep

gosling

piglet

horses

foal

goat

lamb

goose

Visit to Uphill Farm

one	more than one (plural)	baby
horse		
	pigs	kid
sheep		
	geese	

pig

That was good fun.

Parent point: It is important that children understand that words do not always follow set patterns, and can change in the plural. Draw your child's attention to unusual plurals.

A goose on the loose

Can you read this story out loud to a grown-up?

The visitors were enjoying their picnic lunches in the field when George Carter came rushing up to them.

"A goose is on the loose!" he said.
"Has anybody seen the goose?"

Where's the goose?

It's over there.

What's that noise?

Look!

It's on the pond.

No, it's behind that bush.

Is that it in the grass?

I can see it in the barn.

"I heard a funny noise in the long grass," someone said. They all rushed to look, but…

George laughed,

"That's not a goose,
Can't you see?
A goose doesn't buzz –
That's a bee!"

"I heard a funny noise in the barn," someone said. They all rushed to look, but…

George laughed,

"That's not a goose,
You know of course.
A goose doesn't neigh –
That's a horse!"

"I heard a funny noise behind the hedge,"
someone said. They all rushed to look, but…

George laughed,

"That's not a goose,
Take a good look now.
A goose doesn't moo –
That's a cow!"

"I heard a funny noise in the reeds by the pond," someone
said. They all rushed to look, but…

George laughed,

"That's not a goose,
We're out of luck.
A goose doesn't quack –
That's a duck!"

"I can hear a funny noise in Puzzle Wood," someone said. They all rushed to look and…

…everybody laughed.

Goodbye to the Carter family

Grandfather and Grandmother Carter
Katy and George's grandparents

Mrs Carter
Katy and George's mother

Mr Carter
Katy and George's father

Tiptoes
the Carters' cat

Tricks
the Carters' sheepdog

Katy
Mr and Mrs Carter's daughter

George
Mr and Mrs Carter's son

What can you remember about the Carter family
of Uphill Farm?

Who works in the dairy?

Who drives the tractor?

How does Katy help her parents?

Where does Tiptoes like to sleep?

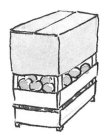

What does Grandmother Carter
sell at the market?

Why does Mr Carter have to get
up early?

What job does Tricks do on the
farm?

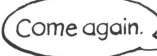

Come again.

Who is your favourite person at Uphill Farm?
Can you say why?

Parent point: Children love to discuss what they have read with you.
Encourage your child to draw pictures of your own family and to write about them.

The children go back to school

After their visit to Uphill Farm, the children are back at school making a model. They have learned Grandfather Carter's harvest song and have been writing stories about the lost goose.

Do you like to write stories?

The children are learning some farm words, using their dictionaries.
Do you know what the words mean?
Tick the right meaning.

herd   to jump over fences ☐

to collect animals together ☐

to chase animals ☐

churn   to stir about ☐

to make bread ☐

to pour out ☐

tractor   a school bus ☐

a farm vehicle ☐

a wheelbarrow ☐

gosling   a baby elephant ☐

a baby rabbit ☐

a baby goose ☐

You know a lot of interesting words.

harvest   time to plant seeds ☐

time to dig the garden ☐

time to bring in the crops ☐

Parent point: It's important that children learn how to use a dictionary to check meanings.
Talk about the meanings of words with your child.

Look at books

Do you remember the story about the goose
on the loose? It was Sarah who found the goose.
Now she is reading a book about a goose.
What do you think she will find in this book?

This is the front cover.

Title

The Great Grey Goose

Author — by Gordon Gander

Publisher — Gosling Books

What is the book called?
Who wrote the book?

This is the back cover.

Information about
the book

An exciting story about a
grey goose who has no
friends and nowhere to live.
What will Grey Goose do?

Does Grey Goose
have many friends?

This is the contents page.

Contents	page
Chapter 1 Grey Goose is lonely	5
Chapter 2 Grey Goose looks for a friend	17
Chapter 3 Grey Goose finds a home	26
Chapter 4 Grey Goose lays an egg	39

Books are great!

How many chapters does the book have?
Which word tells you that Grey Goose
was unhappy?
On which page does **Chapter 3** begin?

Read the contents page again.
Can you tell the story of Grey Goose?

Skills checklist

pages

2   Can read (with help) and discuss subject read ☐

3   Has basic alphabet skills ☐

4   Can read (with help) and discuss subject read ☐

5   Can link reading and writing ☐

6   Can read (with help) and discuss subject read ☐

7   Can distinguish **ch** and **sh** sounds and link reading and spelling skills ☐

8   Can read (with help) and discuss subject read ☐

9   Can use picture clues to write answers to questions on material read ☐

10   Can read (with help) and discuss subject read ☐

11   Can use material read as a stimulus for own writing ☐

12   Can read (with help) and discuss subject read ☐

13   Can extract information from text ☐

14   Can read (with help) and discuss subject read ☐

15   Can read and remember a simple rhyme ☐

pages

16   Can read (with help) and discuss subject read ☐

17   Can draw conclusions from material read and apply this to answer further questions ☐

18   Can read (with help) and discuss subject read ☐

19   Can extract information from non-fiction text and answer questions using picture clues ☐

20   Can read (with help) and discuss subject read ☐

21   Understands that words do not always follow a regular pattern ☐

22–26   Can read a story aloud (with help) ☐

27   Can remember and discuss material read ☐

28   Can answer questions on material read ☐

29   Able to define clearly (using a dictionary if necessary) words met in reading material ☐

30–31   Understands how books work ☐